C000133373

Key Stage 2

Geometry & Measurement

Hilary Koll and Steve Mills

Name _____

Schofield & Sims

Introduction

The world is full of different kinds of shapes, and it is useful to know their names and how to describe them. In this book you will learn about shapes in both two and three dimensions, angles, co-ordinates, symmetry and units of measurement and time.

How to use this book

Before you start using this book, write your name in the name box on the first page.

Then decide how to begin. If you want a complete course on geometry and measurement, you should work right through the book from beginning to end. Another way to use the book is to dip into it when you want to find out about a particular topic, such as quadrilaterals. The Contents page will help you to find the pages you need.

Whichever way you choose, don't try to do too much at once – it's better to work through the book in short bursts.

When you have found the topic you want to study, look out for these icons, which mark different parts of the text.

This icon shows you the activities that you should complete. You write your answers in the spaces provided. You might find it useful to have some spare paper to work on for some of the activities. After you have worked through all the activities on the page, turn to pages 45–49 at the end of the book to check your answers. When you are sure that you understand the topic, put a tick in the box beside it on the Contents page.

On pages 10, 16, 23 and 33 you will find **Progress tests**. These contain questions that will check your understanding of the topics that you have worked through so far. Check your answers on page 50. It is important that you correct any mistakes before moving on to the next section.

On pages 41–44 you will find a **Final test**. This will check your understanding of all the topics. Check your answers on page 51.

Explanation

This text explains the topic and gives examples. Make sure you read it before you start the activities.

This text gives you useful background information about the subject.

Contents

2-D shapes 1

Explanation

The name '**2-D shape**' means 'two-dimensional shape'. This means shapes like squares, triangles and circles. They are **flat** shapes without thickness. These shapes have two dimensions – length and width. They don't have the third dimension of depth, like cubes, cuboids and cylinders which are called **3-D shapes**.

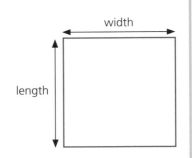

These are the names of some of the 2-D shapes you should know.

Circle – **1** curved side

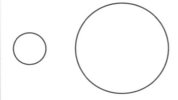

Triangle – **3** straight sides

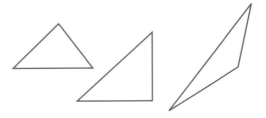

Rectangle – **4** right angles and **4** straight sides

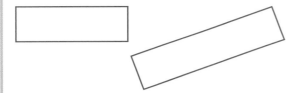

Square – **4** right angles and **4** straight sides of equal length

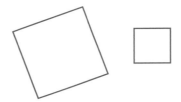

Pentagon – **5** straight sides

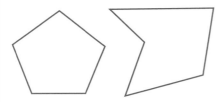

Hexagon – **6** straight sides

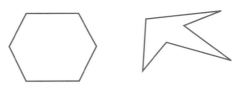

Octagon – **8** straight sides

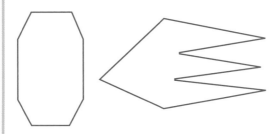

Decagon – **10** straight sides

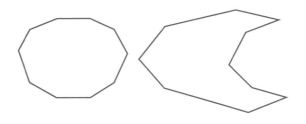

2-D shapes 2

Explanation

Classifying 2-D shapes

You can sort shapes by looking at their **sides** and **corners**. Another word for a **corner** is a **vertex**, and **corners** are **vertices**.

Example A pentagon has **5** straight sides and **5** corners (or vertices).

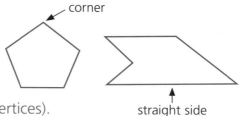

corner

straight side

Activities

1 Complete this table.

Shape	Number of sides	Number of vertices	Straight or curved?
circle			
triangle			
rectangle			
square			
pentagon			
hexagon			
octagon			
decagon			

Regular and irregular polygons

Polygons where all their sides are the same length **and** all their angles are equal are called **regular** polygons.

The sides of an **irregular** polygon are **not** all the same length and its angles are **not** all the same size.

regular hexagon

irregular hexagon

Did you know?

2-D shapes with straight sides are known as **polygons**.

2 Colour all the **regular** polygons.

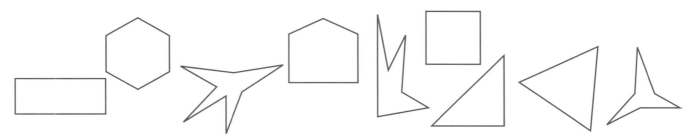

Angles 1

Explanation

An angle is an amount of turn that you measure in **degrees**. Each angle is a fraction of a whole turn, which is **360** degrees. The symbol for degrees is °.

45°

Types of angle

An angle of **90°** (a quarter turn) is called a **right angle**.

An angle of less than **90°** is called an **acute angle**.

An angle of **180°** (a half turn) is called a **straight angle**.

An angle between **90°** and **180°** is called an **obtuse angle**.

An angle between **180°** and **360°** is called a **reflex angle**.

Activities

1 Name these angles.

a

_____

b
_____

c
_____

d
_____

e

_____

f

_____

g
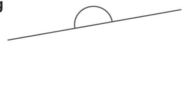
_____

h
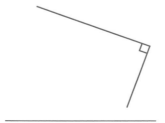
_____

i
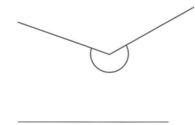
_____

Triangles

Explanation

Some of the sides and angles of triangles can be the same size.

If all the sides are the same length and all the angles are the same the triangle is called an **equilateral triangle**.

If two of the sides are the same length and two of the angles are the same the triangle is called an **isosceles triangle**.

If no sides or angles are the same (all three are different) the triangle is called a **scalene triangle**.

Activities

1 Write whether each triangle is **equilateral**, **isosceles** or **scalene**.

a 　　b 　　c 　　d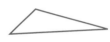

_____　_____　_____　_____

e 　　f 　　g 　　h

_____　_____　_____　_____

If two sides are at right angles to each other we say they are '**perpendicular**'. A triangle with two perpendicular sides is known as a **right-angled** triangle.

2 Tick which of these pairs of lines are **perpendicular**.

a ☐　　b ☐　　c ☐　　d ☐　　e ☐

3 Look at the triangles in activity **1**. Which are right-angled triangles?　_____

Quadrilaterals

Explanation

Shapes with four straight sides are known as **quadrilaterals**. There are different types.

- A **parallelogram** has **2** sets of parallel lines.
- A **rectangle** has **4** right angles. It is a type of parallelogram.
- A **square** has **4** right angles and **4** sides of equal length. It is a type of rectangle.
- A **rhombus** has **2** sets of parallel lines and **4** sides of equal length. It is a type of parallelogram.
- A **trapezium** has **1** set of parallel lines (one of the parallel lines is longer than the other).
- A **kite** has **2** short sides adjacent and of equal length and **2** longer ones adjacent and of equal length.

Did you know?

If two lines are the same distance apart along their whole length we say they are 'parallel'. They do not need to be the same length as each other. No matter how long the lines are extended, they would never meet.

Activities

1 Write which of the quadrilaterals below is a:

a parallelogram b rectangle c square

_____   _____   _____

d rhombus e trapezium f kite

_____   _____   _____

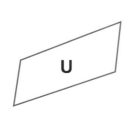
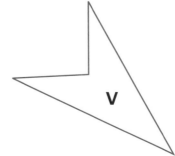
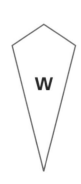

Reflective symmetry

Explanation

A shape has **reflective symmetry** when it can be reflected in one or more mirror lines. These are called its **lines of symmetry**.

These shapes all have reflective symmetry because they have one or more lines of symmetry.

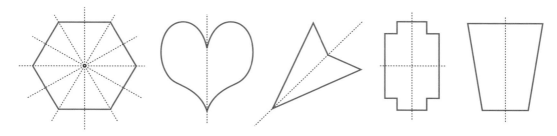

Activities

1 Draw any lines of **reflective symmetry** on these shapes. Remember there may be more than one line, or there may be none at all.

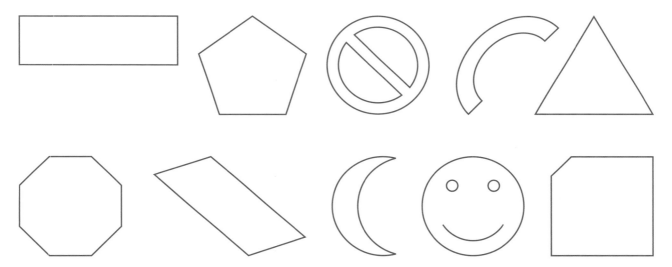

2 Tick any of the following shapes that have reflective symmetry.

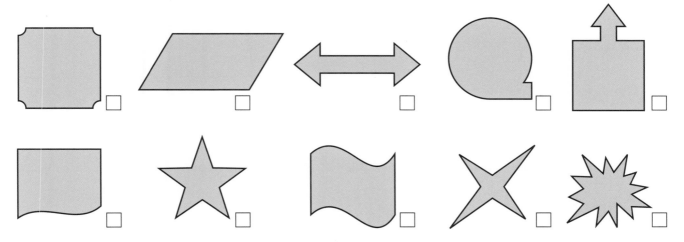

Progress test 1

1 Write the name of each of these shapes.

a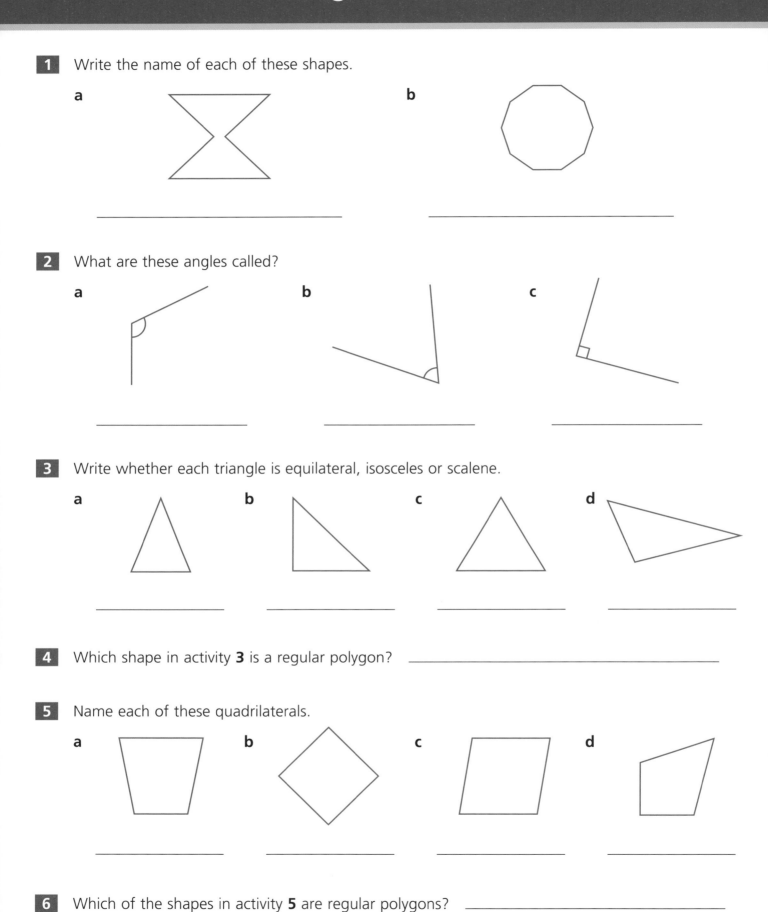

b

_____

_____

2 What are these angles called?

a

b

c

_____

_____

_____

3 Write whether each triangle is equilateral, isosceles or scalene.

a

b

c

d

_____

_____

_____

_____

4 Which shape in activity **3** is a regular polygon? _____

5 Name each of these quadrilaterals.

a

b

c

d

_____

_____

_____

_____

6 Which of the shapes in activity **5** are regular polygons? _____

7 Draw all the lines of reflective symmetry in the shapes in activities **3** and **5** above.

Geometry & Measurement

Co-ordinates 1

Explanation

Co-ordinates allow you to pinpoint exactly where a point or shape is on a graph or map.

Co-ordinates are written in brackets separated by a comma, like this (**3**, **2**). They are an 'ordered pair' of numbers, which means the order in which they are written is important.

The **first** number is the *x* **co-ordinate**, which shows how many places **across** to move on the horizontal axis. The second number is the *y* **co-ordinate**, which shows how many places **up** or **down** to move on the vertical axis.

Remember the position of the axes by saying '*x* is a cross' because the *x* axis goes across.

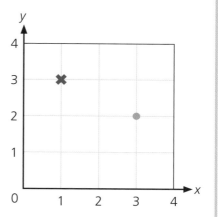

The dot is at (**3**, **2**) and the cross is at (**1**, **3**).

Activities

1 Write the **co-ordinates** of the positions of these letters on the grid below.

a P (____ , ____)

b Q (____ , ____)

c R (____ , ____)

d S (____ , ____)

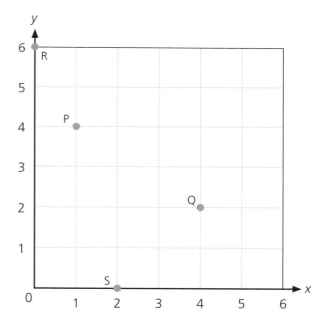

2 Mark these letters on the grid above.

a J at (**6**, **3**)   **b** K at (**2**, **5**)   **c** L at (**3**, **4**)   **d** M at (**5**, **1**)

Did you know?

Co-ordinates were invented by René Descartes, a French scientist and mathematician, in the seventeenth century.

Translations

Explanation

A **translation** is a movement of a shape in a particular direction. It is like sliding a shape without turning it or changing its size or angles.

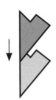 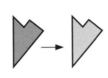 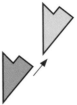

When translating shapes on a co-ordinate grid, take each of the vertices and move them one at a time. Use the co-ordinates (x, y) of each vertex to help you to check where the new position should be.

- If translating to the right, add to the x co-ordinate.
- If translating to the left, subtract from the x co-ordinate.
- If translating up, add to the y co-ordinate.
- If translating down, subtract from the y co-ordinate.

Activities

1 Write the co-ordinates of each triangle shown and then draw the **translation** given.

(__ , __) (__ , __) (__ , __) (__ , __) (__ , __) (__ , __) (__ , __) (__ , __) (__ , __)

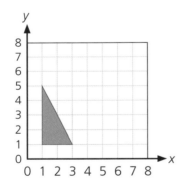 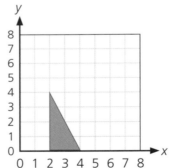 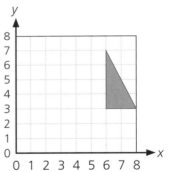

a **3** squares to the right **b** **2** squares to the right and **4** squares up **c** **5** squares to the left and **3** squares down

2 A shape has the co-ordinates (**1, 3**) (**2, 5**) (**5, 6**). Write its new co-ordinates after a translation of:

a **2** squares to the right (____ , ____) (____ , ____) (____ , ____)

b **4** squares up (____ , ____) (____ , ____) (____ , ____)

c **1** square to the left and **2** squares down. (____ , ____) (____ , ____) (____ , ____)

Geometry & Measurement

Angles 2

Explanation

A **protractor** (sometimes called an angle measurer) is used to measure the size of an angle, like this.

- Line up the centre with the point where the two lines meet.
- Turn the protractor until one of the lines is along a zero line.
- Count around from zero, in tens and units, until you reach the other line.
- Read the scale carefully. Sometimes you might have to extend the lines with a pencil and ruler.

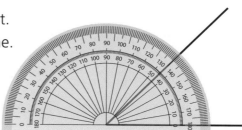

Activities

1 Use a protractor to measure the size of these angles.

a

_____

b

_____

c

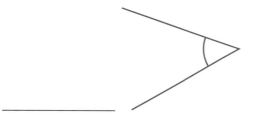

_____

d

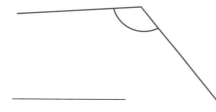

_____

e

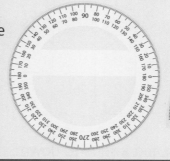

_____

Did you know?

Thousands of years ago it was thought that the Earth took about **360** days to orbit the sun.

That is why there are **360** degrees in a circle.

A circular protractor shows **360** degrees.

A semi-circular protractor shows **180** degrees.

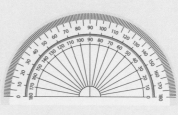

3-D shapes 1

Explanation

The name '**3-D shape**' means 'three-dimensional shape'. This includes shapes like cubes, cuboids and cylinders. They are shapes with **thickness**. These shapes have three dimensions, or measurements – length, width and depth. 3-D shapes are called **solid** shapes, even though they can be solid or hollow.

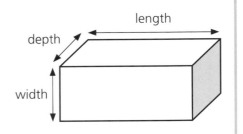

These are the names of some of the 3-D shapes you should know.

Cube

Cuboid
(rectangular prism)

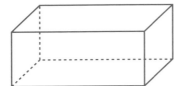

Cone

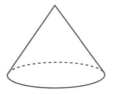

Cylinder
(circular prism)

Prism

A prism has the same **cross-section** along its length. This cross-section can be any of the 2-D shapes. Think of a prism as a 2-D shape that has been stretched to make a 3-D shape.

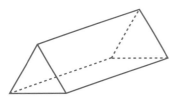

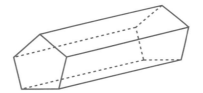

triangular
prism

pentagonal
prism

Pyramid

A pyramid has a 2-D base, like a square, triangle or pentagon. The other **faces** are triangles and join together at a **vertex**.

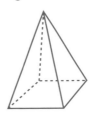

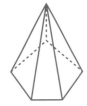

square-based
pyramid

pentagonal-based
pyramid

Activities

1 Write the names of these shapes.

a

b

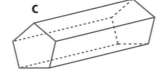
c

d

e

_____   _____   _____   _____   _____

3-D shapes 2

Explanation

Properties of 3-D shapes

You will need to know these words.

Face – a flat or curved surface

Edge – where two faces meet

Vertex – a corner or point

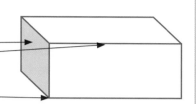

Activities

1 Complete this table. Add a different shape to the bottom row.

Name of shape	Number of faces (F)	Number of vertices (V)	Number of edges (E)
sphere			
cone			
cylinder			
cube			
cuboid			
triangular prism			
square-based pyramid			

There is a relationship between the number of faces, vertices and edges in all flat-faced shapes such as cubes, cuboids, prisms and pyramids (but not spheres or cylinders).

The number of **faces** plus the number of **vertices** equals the number of **edges** plus two.

This is simplified to: F + V = E + 2

Did you know?

This relationship was discovered by a mathematician called Euler. It is known as **Euler's Theorem**.

2 Use Euler's Theorem for these shapes.

Shape	F	V	E + 2
cube			
cuboid			
triangular prism			
square-based pyramid			

Progress test 2

1 Write the co-ordinates of the letters:

   a E (____,____)   **b** F (____,____)   **c** G (____,____)

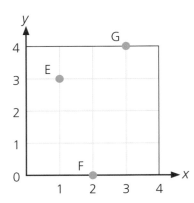

2 Mark these letters on the grid.

   a J at (**4, 1**)   **b** K at (**2, 4**)   **c** L at (**0, 1**)

3 A shape has the co-ordinates (**2, 4**) (**2, 6**) (**6, 6**). Write its new co-ordinates after a translation of:

   a **2** squares to the right (____,____) (____,____) (____,____)

   b **3** squares up (____,____) (____,____) (____,____)

   c **1** square to the left and **2** squares down (____,____) (____,____) (____,____)

4 Use a protractor to measure the size of these angles.

   a

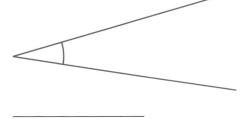

   _____

   b

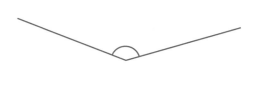

   _____

5 Write the names of these 3-D shapes.

   a   **b**   **c**   **d**

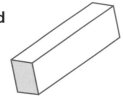

   _____   _____   _____   _____

6 Write the number of faces, vertices and edges of these shapes.

   a   **b**   **c**

Cube		Square-based pyramid		Hexagonal prism
faces _____		faces _____		faces _____
vertices _____		vertices _____		vertices _____
edges _____		edges _____		edges _____

Geometry & Measurement

Drawing and making shapes

To draw a 2-D shape, use a ruler and a protractor. If given the lengths of the sides, draw them accurately with the ruler. If given angles, use the protractor to help you mark them correctly.

To make a 3-D shape, you can use a 'net' that folds up to create the shape.

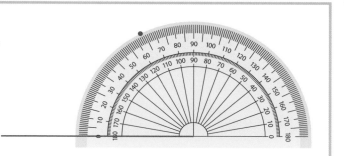

Activities

1 Draw a **right-angled** triangle with lengths of **6**cm, **8**cm and **10**cm. The **6**cm line has been drawn for you already.

6cm

2 Draw an angle of **65°** to complete a triangle.

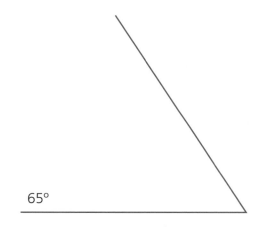

65°

3 Tick which of these nets would fold to make a cube.

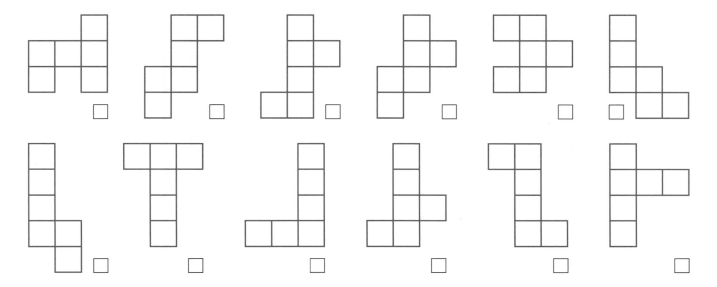

Co-ordinates 2

Explanation

Co-ordinates in four quadrants

Co-ordinates can have negative numbers like these: (**−4, 3**), (**3, −2**) or (**−1, −4**). You just need a grid with negative numbers on the *x* and *y* axes.

The top-right quarter of this grid is the same as the grid on page 11. The *x* and *y* axes have continued past **0** into negative numbers. This creates three more sections, called **quadrants**.

Example The letter **A** is at (**2, 3**), **B** is at (**3, −3**), **C** is at (**−2, −1**) and **D** is at (**−4, 3**).

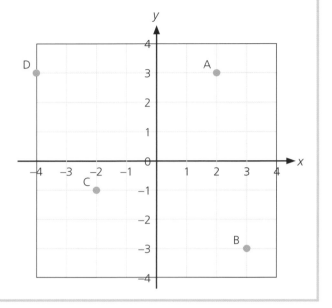

Activities

1 Write the co-ordinates of the positions of these letters on the grid.

   a P (____, ____)   **b** R (____, ____)

   c S (____, ____)   **d** T (____, ____)

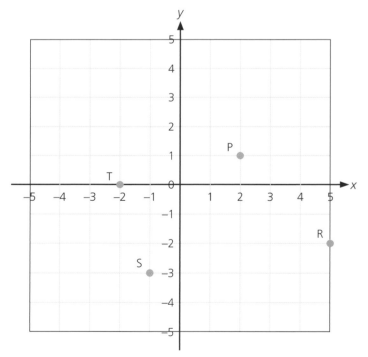

2 Mark these letters on the grid.

   a J at (**4, 2**)   **b** K at (**1, −3**)

   c L at (**−3, −4**)   **d** M at (**−5, 2**)

Reflecting patterns and shapes 1

Explanation

When you see something in a mirror you see its **reflection**. The reflection or new shape is called the **image**. You can reflect patterns and shapes in **mirror lines**. Mirror lines can be in any direction, like this.

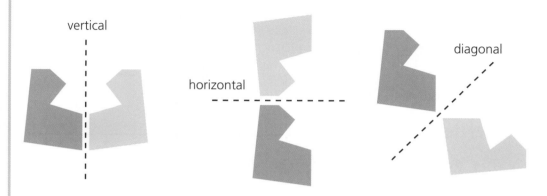

Notice that each corner of the dark shape is the same distance from the mirror line as the corner of the lighter image.

Activities

1 Colour the reflections of these patterns.

a
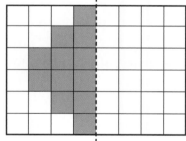

b
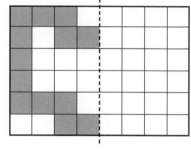

c
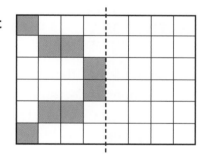

d
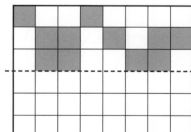

e
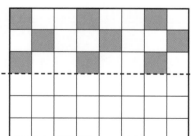

f
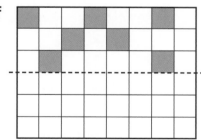

g
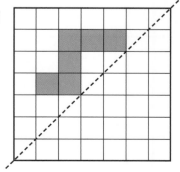

h
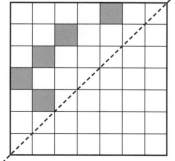

i
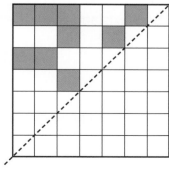

Reflecting patterns and shapes 2

Explanation

Patterns occur in the co-ordinates when reflecting shapes in the axes of a co-ordinate grid. Shape A has been reflected in the vertical *y* axis to form Shape B and in the horizontal *x* axis to form Shape C.

Look at the patterns in these co-ordinates (*x*, *y*).

Co-ordinates of Shape A   (**1, 2**) (**2, 2**) (**1, 4**)

Co-ordinates of Shape B   (**−1, 2**) (**−2, 2**) (**−1, 4**)

The *x* co-ordinates change from positive to negative or vice versa after a reflection in the *y* axis. If the *x* co-ordinate is zero it doesn't change.

Co-ordinates of Shape A   (**1, 2**) (**2, 2**) (**1, 4**)

Co-ordinates of Shape C   (**1, −2**) (**2, −2**) (**1, −4**)

The *y* co-ordinates change from positive to negative or vice versa after a reflection in the *x* axis. If the *y* co-ordinate is zero it doesn't change.

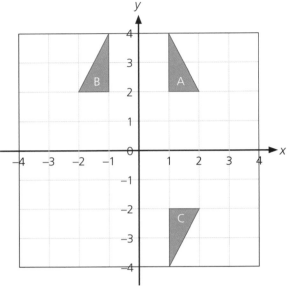

Activities

1 Shape D has the co-ordinates (**3, 1**) (**3, 4**) (**1, 3**). Write the co-ordinates of Shape D when it has been reflected in the:

a *y* axis   (____ , ____) (____ , ____) (____ , ____)

b *x* axis   (____ , ____) (____ , ____) (____ , ____)

2 Reflect Shape A in the:

a *x* axis and mark the new Shape B

b *y* axis and mark the new Shape C

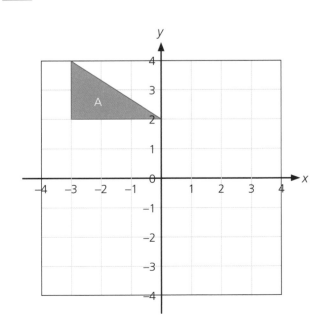

3 Reflect Shape B in the *y* axis and mark the new Shape D.

Calculating angles

Explanation

The size of missing angles can be calculated, rather than measured. If you use the information below, you can subtract given angles to find the size of missing ones.

Angles on a straight line

There are **180°** in a straight angle: $a + b = $ **180°**.

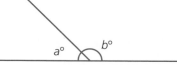

Angles at a point

There are **360°** in a full turn: $c + d + e = $ **360°**.

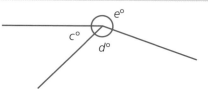

Angles in a triangle

The three angles of a triangle add up to **180°**. You can prove this by tearing a triangle into three pieces, with a corner in each.

Join the corners together to make a straight line. You know there are **180°** in a straight angle, so there must be **180°** in a triangle.

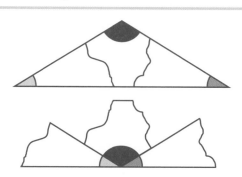

Activities

1 **Calculate** the missing angles.

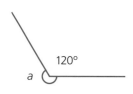 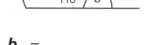 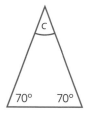 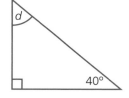

a = _____ b = _____ c = _____ d = _____

2 Solve these problems.

a A triangle has an angle of **88°** and an angle of **25°**.
What is the size of its third angle and is it acute or obtuse?   _____ _____

b Robin stands and faces North. He turns clockwise through **170°** and then turns clockwise through **60°**. Through what angle must he still turn clockwise to face North again?   _____

c A right-angled triangle has an angle of **55°**.
What is the size of the third angle?   _____

d An isosceles triangle has two angles of **77°**.
What is the size of the third angle?   _____

Circles

Explanation

There are special words related to the lines and edges of circles.

The **radius** is the distance from the edge to the centre of the circle. It is half the size of the **diameter** which is the widest distance across the circle, through the centre.

The **circumference** is the distance around the circle. Part of the circumference is called an **arc**.

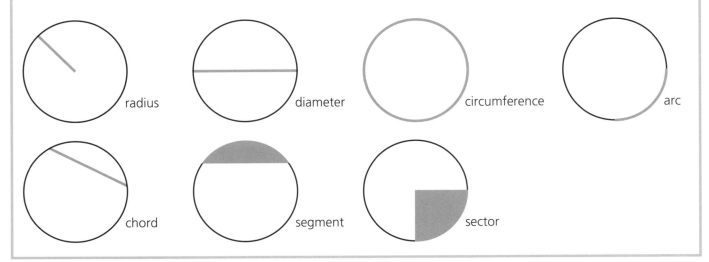

Activities

1 Answer these questions.

a What is the name of the line from one side of a circle to the other, passing through the centre of the circle? _____

b If the radius of a circle is **5**cm, what is its diameter? _____

c If the diameter of a circle is **8**cm, what is its radius? _____

d A circle has a circumference of **27**cm. An arc, marked on the circle, is one-third of the length of the circumference. What is the length of the arc? _____

e A circle has an area of **24**cm². A diameter is drawn on it, splitting the circle into two segments. What is the area of each segment? _____

f Name the line from one side of a circle to the other that does **not** go through the centre of the circle. _____

g Two radii (plural of 'radius') and an arc are drawn on a circle, creating an area shaped like a slice of pizza. What is the special name for this area? _____

Progress test 3

1 Colour the reflections of these patterns.

a

b

c

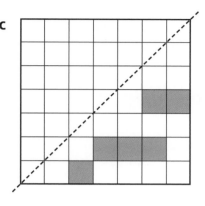

2 Write the co-ordinates of the letters.

a P (___ , ___)   **b** Q (___ , ___)

3 Mark these letters on the grid.

a R at (**−4**, **1**)   **b** S at (**2**, **−4**)

c T at (**−3**, **−2**)   **d** U at (**0**, **−3**)

4 Calculate the missing angles.

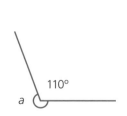

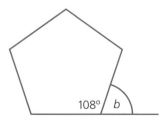

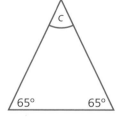

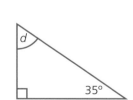

a = _____   *b* = _____   *c* = _____   *d* = _____

5 Solve these problems.

a What is the special name of the perimeter of a circle?   _____

b If the diameter of a circle is **7**cm, what is its radius?   _____

c If the radius of a circle is **8**cm, what is its diameter?   _____

Length

Explanation

To find how long something is, you measure its **length**. There are lots of different words to describe how long something is such as length, depth, height, width, distance, breadth, perimeter, circumference, diameter, radius and thickness.

Length is usually measured in these metric units: **millimetres (mm)**, **centimetres (cm)**, **metres (m)** and **kilometres (km)**.

10mm = **1**cm   **100**cm = **1**m   **1000**m = **1**km

Length can also be measured in feet, yards or miles (known as Imperial units).

Activities

1   You will need a ruler and five small objects to measure. Estimate their length first and then measure them. Complete the table.

Object	My estimate (cm)	Its length (cm)	Difference (cm)

2   Colour the best estimate for the length of each item.

a

| 15mm |
| 15cm |
| 15km |

b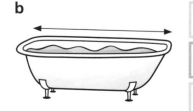

| 180cm |
| 18cm |
| 1800cm |

c

| 1700m |
| 1.7km |
| 17m |

Mass

Explanation

To find out how heavy something is you measure its **mass**. Mass is the amount of matter an object is made from. It is different from weight.

Mass is usually measured in **grams (g)** and **kilograms (kg)**. **1000**g = **1**kg.

grams	kilograms
light things, like tins of soup, flour, cheese …	heavy things, like people, bags of potatoes, coal …

Mass can also be measured in ounces, pounds or stones (known as Imperial units).

Did you know?

If you stood on the moon your weight would be less because weight is caused by the pull of gravity, and there is less gravity on the moon. Your mass would stay the same because your body would be the same.

Activities

1 You will need a set of weighing scales and five objects to be weighed. Estimate first and then weigh them. Complete the table.

Object	My estimate (g)	Its mass (g)	Difference (g)

2 Colour the best estimate for each item.

a

1g
1kg
10kg

b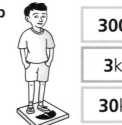

300g
3kg
30kg

c

1kg
10kg
100kg

Capacity

Explanation

The **capacity** of something, like a cup or a bath, is the amount it can hold when it is full.

Capacity is usually measured in **litres (l)** and **millilitres (ml)** and also in Imperial units like pints and gallons.

millilitres	litres	
small things, like cups and spoons…	larger things, like bottles, buckets and baths…	**1000**ml = **1**l

Activities

1 You will need five containers such as cups, teapots and bottles, as well as a measuring jug. First, fill a container with water. Estimate its capacity, and then empty it into the measuring jug to find its actual capacity in millilitres. Do this for each of your containers, and complete the table.

Object	My estimate (ml)	Its capacity (ml)	Difference (ml)

2 Colour the best estimate for each item.

a

25ml
250ml
2l

b

300ml
30ml
3ml

c

50ml
500ml
5l

Converting between units of measurement

Explanation

It is important to know how many of one unit makes up another.

Length

10mm = **1**cm

100cm = **1**m

1000m = **1**km

Capacity

1000ml = **1**l

100cl = **1**l

Mass

1000g = **1**kg

1000kg = **1** tonne

Time

60 seconds = **1** minute   **60** minutes = **1** hour

24 hours = **1** day   **7** days = **1** week

52 weeks = **1** year   **365** or **366** days = **1** year

10 years = **1** decade   **100** years = **1** century

Converting between metric units

You can use these diagrams to help convert one unit to another.

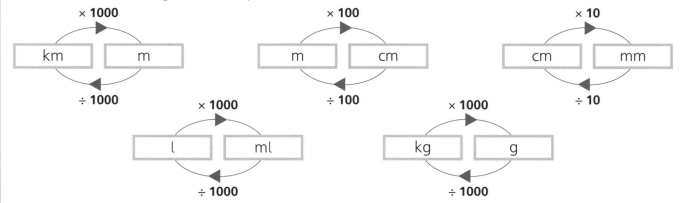

Activities

1 Convert these measurements.

a 63m   = _____ cm   **b** 450cm = _____ m   **c** 3170ml = _____ l

d 10l   = _____ ml   **e** 4500g = _____ kg   **f** 5.25kg = _____ g

g 4780cm = _____ m   **h** 3875ml = _____ l   **i** 7820g   = _____ kg

2 Cover the boxes above and complete these sentences.

a One metre is _____ centimetres.   **b** One kilometre is _____ metres.

c One kilogram is _____ grams.   **d** One litre is _____ millilitres.

e One centimetre is _____ millimetres. **f** One metre is _____ millimetres.

Problems involving length, mass and capacity

Explanation

When adding measurements, make sure that they are given in the same unit. If not, change them so that they are. It is usually easier to change them to the smaller of the units so, if you have kilograms and grams, change them to grams. If you have millilitres and litres, change them to millilitres.

Example James walked **1200**m in the morning and **2**km in the afternoon. How far did he walk altogether?

One measurement is in metres and the other is in kilometres. **1200**m + **2**km

Change kilometres to metres. **1200**m + **2000**m = **3200**m

Activities

1 Convert these measurements.

a **5.2**kg = _____ g

b **1.8**l = _____ ml

c **7000**g = _____ kg

d **900**ml = _____ l

e **52**mm = _____ cm

f **0.23**m = _____ cm

g **13 000**g = _____ kg

h **8500**ml = _____ l

2 Solve these measurement problems.

a I have a **1**-litre bottle of water. I drink **400**ml. How much is left? _____

b I have a piece of string that is **3**m long. I cut off a piece that is **60**cm. How much string remains? _____

c A seed begins to grow. After two days the shoot is **8**mm tall. It grows a further **2.2**cm over the next two days. How tall is it now? _____

d The distance from Clare's home to school is **5800**m. She cycles to school one day and stops after **2**km. How much further has she to go? _____

e Three items weigh **3**kg, **300**g and **0.7**kg. What is the total mass of the three items? _____

f What is the total length of a line that is **8**mm longer than **5.7**cm? _____

g A tin holds **1.2** litres of paint. Mia pours out **700** millilitres of it. How much is still in the tin? _____

Geometry & Measurement

Reading scales

Explanation

Follow these steps when reading scales on measuring instruments.

Step 1: Choose two adjacent (next to each other) numbers and find the difference between them.

Step 2: Count how many small intervals (spaces) there are between these numbers.

Step 3: Work out, by dividing, how much each of these intervals is worth.

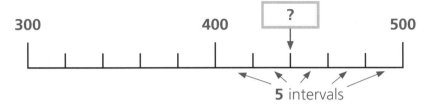

The difference between 400 and 500 is 100. There are 5 intervals. Each interval is worth **20** (**100 ÷ 5**), so the arrow is pointing to **440** (**400 + 20 + 20**).

Activities

1   Write the numbers in the boxes to show what is being pointed to on these scales.

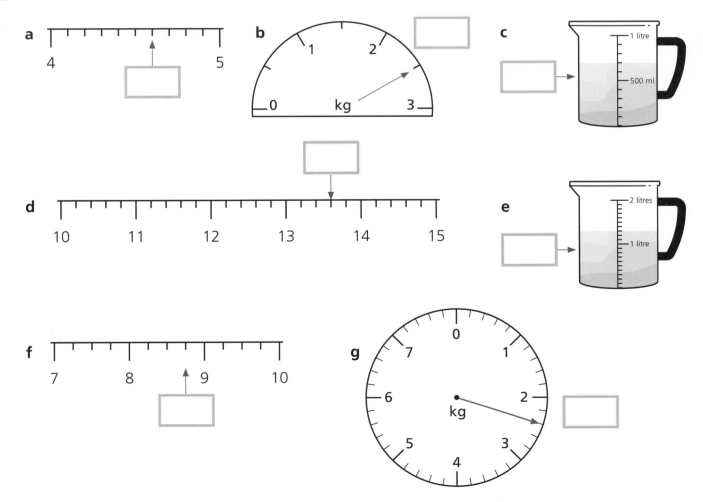

Perimeter

Explanation

Perimeters of rectangles

The **perimeter** is the distance around the outside of a 2-D shape. The perimeter is measured in centimetres (cm), metres (m) or kilometres (km). The perimeter of this rectangle is **14**cm.

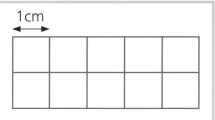

1cm

Example The perimeter of the rectangle below is **15**cm + **8**cm + **15**cm + **8**cm = **46**cm.

As the opposite sides of a rectangle are the same length, you can find the perimeter if you know the lengths of two of the sides. You can write this as a formula in different ways.

2 × length + 2 × width or **2l + 2w** or **2(l + w)**

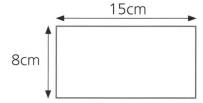

15cm

8cm

Activities

1 Find the perimeter of these rectangles.

a
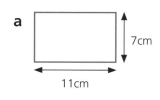
7cm
11cm

b
10cm
15cm

c
18cm
12cm

_____ cm   _____ cm   _____ cm

Perimeters of other shapes

You can find the perimeters of other shapes by adding up the lengths of the sides.

Example The perimeter of this triangle is **6**cm + **9**cm + **10**cm = **25**cm.

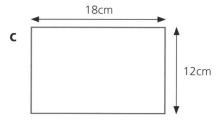

6cm
9cm
10cm

2 Find the perimeter of these shapes.

a
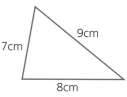
9cm
7cm
8cm

b
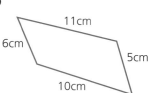
11cm
6cm
5cm
10cm

c
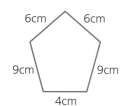
6cm   6cm
9cm   9cm
4cm

d
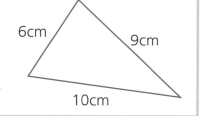
16cm
6cm
16cm
8cm
10cm
8cm

_____ cm   _____ cm   _____ cm   _____ cm

Geometry & Measurement

Time 1

Explanation

It is important to be confident in reading clocks to the nearest minute. Remember there are **60** minutes in an hour. Use this knowledge to help you tell the time and convert between analogue and digital time.

'**Seventeen minutes past ten**' is the same as **10.17**.

'**One minute to four**' is the same as '**59 minutes after 3**' or **3.59**.

'**22 minutes to two**' is the same as '**38 minutes after 1**' or **1.38**.

Activities

1 Write these as digital times. All the clocks show times in the morning.

a

b

c

_____   _____   _____

2 Join pairs of clocks showing the same times.

Explanation

12-hour clocks

In **12-hour** clocks you use **a.m.** to show times between midnight and midday (morning) and **p.m.** to show times between midday and midnight (afternoon and evening).

If you are using the 12-hour clock you must **always** write a.m. or p.m., for example **11.20 a.m.** (morning) or **11.20 p.m.** (evening).

24-hour clocks

A **24-hour** clock uses the numbers from **0** to **24** to stand for all the hours in the day. **0** is midnight and after midday the hours become **13**, **14**, **15**, **16**, etc. so that **5 p.m.** becomes **17:00** and **9.30 p.m.** is **21:30**. If you are using the 24-hour clock you must **always** write the time using four digits, like **16:45** or **09:10**.

Example These two clocks are showing the same time.

Activities

1 Join pairs of clocks showing the same times.

Progress test 4

1 Colour the best estimate for each item.

a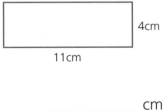

10g
1kg
100kg

b

200ml
2000ml
200l

c

20g
2kg
200kg

2 Fill in the missing numbers.

a   **7**m = _____ cm

b   **2.5**cm = _____ mm

c   **0.6**m = _____ cm

d   **0.8**km = _____ m

3 Solve these measurement problems.

a   I have a **1**-litre bottle of water. I drink **300**ml.
   How much is left?   _____

b   I have a piece of wire that is **4**m long.
   I cut off a piece that is **60**cm. How much string remains? _____

c   A seed begins to grow. After two days the shoot is **6**mm tall.
   It grows a further **2.7**cm over the next two days. How tall is it now? _____

4 Find the perimeter of these shapes.

a
```
         
        4cm
  11cm
```

b
```
      9cm
6cm       6cm
   14cm
```

c
```
      10cm
6cm
   8cm
```

_____ cm   _____ cm   _____ cm

5 Write the same time on the matching clock. All the times are in the morning.

a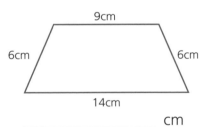

b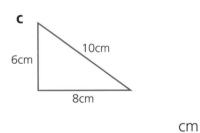

Time 3

Explanation

As you learnt on page 27, you need to know the following **units of time**.

60 seconds = **1** minute	**60** minutes = **1** hour	**24** hours = **1** day
7 days = **1** week	**52** weeks = **1** year	**365** or **366** days = **1** year
12 months = **1** year	**10** years = **1** decade	**100** years = **1** century

Activities

1 Which units of time would you use to measure the following?

   a time until your birthday _____

   b time it takes a kettle to boil _____

   c time an old tree has been alive _____

   d time you sleep each night _____

   e time since the Romans _____

Timetables are lists that give information about when things happen, such as train or bus timetables, or TV listings. The 24-hour clock is often used in timetables to avoid confusion over a.m. and p.m.

To read a timetable, look along a row and down a column to where these meet.

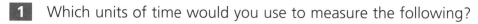

Cinema start times for Friday			
	Screen 1	**Screen 2**	**Screen 3**
Jack Sprat	14:20	15:45	17:50
Infinite Justice	19:50	**20:40**	21:40
Loukos River	18:30	19:45	19:30

2 Answer these questions using the information in the timetable above.

   a When does *Loukos River* start on Screen 3? _____

   b When does *Jack Sprat* start on Screen 2? _____

   c On which screen can you see *Infinite Justice*, after **9** p.m.? _____

   d If you went into Screen 2 at **4** p.m. which film would be showing? _____

Geometry & Measurement

Area 1

Explanation

Area is the amount of surface that a shape covers.
In a 2-D (flat) shape it is the space inside the lines boundary.

In a 3-D (solid) shape it is the total amount of surface of **all** the faces, including the 'hidden' faces. For 3-D shapes this is often called 'surface area'.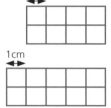

Area is measured in square units, like **square centimetres (cm²)** or **square metres (m²)**.

Finding area

You can find the area of a rectangle by counting the number of squares it covers. The area is **8** centimetre squares or **8**cm².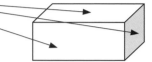

You can also find area by multiplying. This rectangle has **2** rows with **5** squares in each. **2 × 5** is **10**. The area is **10**cm².

Activities

1 Find the area of these rectangles.

a

b

c

_____ squares   _____ squares   _____ squares

Sometimes just the number of squares along two sides are given.
Multiply to find the area: **3**cm × **5**cm = **15**cm²

You have just used the formula:
the area of a rectangle = length × width.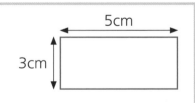

---

2 Use the formula to find the area of these rectangles.

a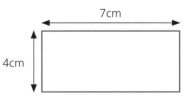

b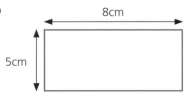

c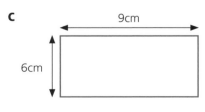

_____ cm²   _____ cm²   _____ cm²

Imperial units

Explanation

On pages 24 to 28 the focus was on **metric units** of length, mass and capacity. Metric units are based on **10**, **100** and **1000**, such as **10**mm = **1**cm and so on. There are other units of measurement known as **Imperial units** which were commonly used in the past and are still used today.

Length	Capacity	Mass
12 inches = **1** foot	**8** pints = **1** gallon	**16** ounces (oz) = **1** pound
3 feet = **1** yard		**14** pounds (lb) = **1** stone
1760 yards = **1** mile		

Activities

A person might weigh themselves using stones and pounds.

1 stone = **14** pounds

9 stone = **9** × **14** pounds = **126** pounds

9 stone **6** pounds = **126** + **6** pounds = **132** pounds

*I weigh **9** stone **6** pounds.*

1 Convert these measurements.

    a **2** feet = _____ inches   **b** **4** yards = _____ feet

    c $\frac{1}{2}$ mile = _____ yards   **d** **2** gallons = _____ pints

    e **10** pounds = _____ ounces   **f** **3** stone = _____ pounds

It is also useful to know the metric equivalents:

Length	Capacity	Mass
2.5cm is about **1** inch	**500**ml ($\frac{1}{2}$ litre) is about **1** pint	**25**g is about **1** ounce
30cm is about **1** foot	**4.5** litres is about **1** gallon	**400**g is about **1** pound
90cm is about **1** yard		**1**kg is about **2.2** pounds
1.6km is about **1** mile		**6**kg is about **1** stone

2 Convert these measurements.

    a **2** miles = _____ km   **b** **10** gallons = _____ l

    c _____ miles = **6.4**km   **d** _____ pounds = **32**kg

Area 2

Explanation

Areas of right-angled triangles

You can use what you know about the area of rectangles to find the area of right-angled triangles. A right-angled triangle is half a rectangle. So, you can find the area of the whole rectangle and then halve this.

Remember that the **area of a rectangle = length × width**.

6 × 10 = 60, so **60 ÷ 2 = 30**

Another way is to halve one of the measurements in the triangle before multiplying.

Instead of halving the answer to **6 × 10,** do **3 × 10** or **6 × 5**. In each case the answer is **30**.

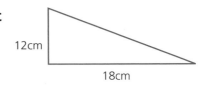

10cm

6cm

Area of triangle = 30cm²

Activities

1 Find the area of these triangles.

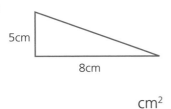

a
5cm
8cm

_____ cm²

b
10cm
6cm

_____ cm²

c
12cm
18cm

_____ cm²

Areas of other shapes

You can find the area of shapes like these by splitting them into rectangles.

Find the area of each and add the answers together.

7cm × **6**cm = **42**cm²

8cm × **12**cm = **96**cm², **42 + 96 =138**, so the area of the shape is **138**cm².

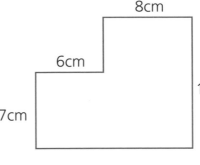

8cm
6cm
12cm
7cm

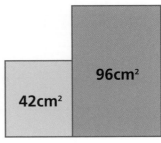

96cm²
42cm²

2 Find the area of these shapes by splitting them into rectangles.

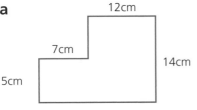

a
12cm
7cm
14cm
5cm

_____ cm²

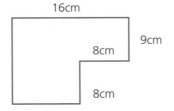

b
16cm
8cm
9cm
8cm

_____ cm²

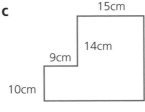

c
15cm
14cm
9cm
10cm

_____ cm²

Volume

Explanation

Volume is the space inside a 3-D shape. It is measured in **centimetre cubes (cm³)** and **metre cubes (m³)**.

Volume can be found by counting cubes or by using length, width and height.

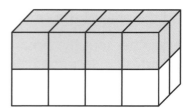

- Count the cubes in one layer: **8 cubes**
- Count how many layers there are: **2 layers**
- Multiply the number of cubes in one layer by the number of layers, **8 × 2 = 16 cubes**

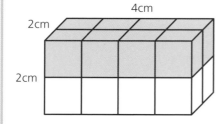

If you know the height, length and width, you can multiply to find the volume.

length = **4**cm, width = **2**cm, height = **2**cm

4 × 2 × 2 = 16   volume = 16cm³

Activities

1 Find the volume of these cuboids by counting cubes. Each cube drawn is **1**cm³.

a

_____ cm³

b

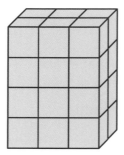

_____ cm³

2 Find the volume of these cuboids using length, width and height.

a

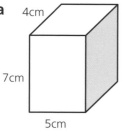
4cm
7cm
5cm

_____ cm³

b

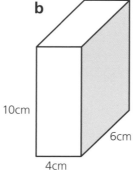
10cm
4cm
6cm

_____ cm³

c

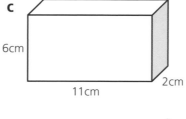
6cm
11cm
2cm

_____ cm³

d

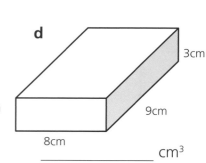
3cm
9cm
8cm

_____ cm³

Time problems

Explanation

On page 34 the main units of time were listed. The diagrams below show how to convert between different units of time. For example, if converting **30** minutes to seconds the first diagram shows that you would multiply the number of minutes by **60**.

30 minutes = **30** × **60** seconds = **1800** seconds

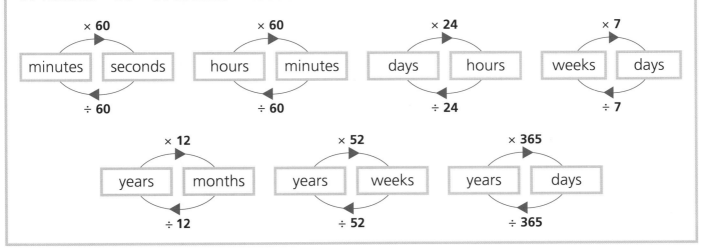

Activities

1 Convert between these units.

a   **2** minutes = _____ seconds

b   **4** hours = _____ minutes

c   **240** hours = _____ days

d   **49** days = _____ weeks

e   **140** days = _____ weeks

f   **3** years = _____ weeks

g   **240** months = _____ years

h   **3** years = _____ days
      (not including leap years)

2 Solve these problems involving converting units of time.

a   Amir's plane is due to take off in **53** hours from now.
     It is now Thursday at **11** a.m. When is Amir's flight?   _____

b   Hannah earns £**200** per month. How much does she
     earn in three years?   _____

c   It is **8** weeks and **6** days until Jake goes on holiday. He decides
     to save £**1** each day until then to use as spending money.
     How much spending money will he end up with?   _____

Area and perimeter

Explanation

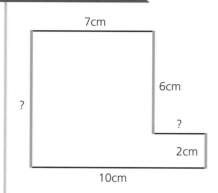

When finding the **areas** and **perimeters** of shapes, it is sometimes necessary to use addition or subtraction to find the lengths of unknown sides. Here the lengths of two sides are unknown.

Notice that the longer purple line is the same length as the two smaller purple lines added together. So the longer purple line must be **6**cm + **2**cm = **8**cm. Similarly the other unknown side is **7**cm less than **10**cm, **10**cm − **7**cm = **3**cm.

Did you know?

The **area** of a two shapes can be the same but they can have different perimeters. The **perimeter** of two shapes can be the same but they can have different areas.

Activities

1 Calculate the missing lengths.

a

8cm
7cm
4cm
?
5cm
12cm

b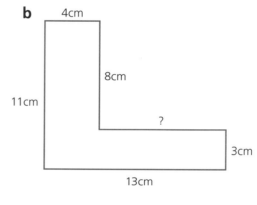

4cm
8cm
11cm
?
3cm
13cm

c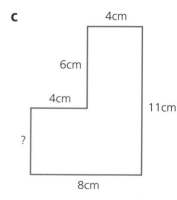

4cm
6cm
4cm
11cm
?
8cm

_____   _____   _____

Once all the sides are known they can be added together to find the perimeter. The areas can also be found by splitting the shape into two rectangles (see page 37).

---

2 Now find the perimeter of each shape in activity **1**.

  a Perimeter = _____

  b Perimeter = _____

  c Perimeter = _____

3 Find the area of each shape in activity **1**.

  a Area = _____

  b Area = _____

  c Area = _____

Final test

1 Give the names of these angles.

a

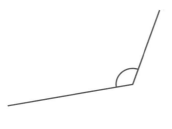

b

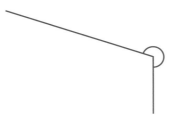

c

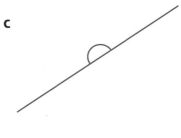

_____   _____   _____

2 Use a protractor to measure the size of these angles.

a

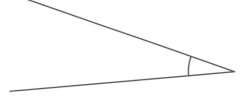

b

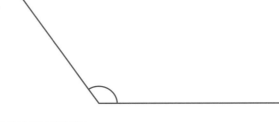

_____   _____

3 Write the number of faces, vertices and edges of these shapes.

a

Cube
faces _____
vertices _____
edges _____

b

Triangle-based pyramid
faces _____
vertices _____
edges _____

c

Pentagonal prism
faces _____
vertices _____
edges _____

4 Write the co-ordinates of the letters:

a E (___ , ___)   b F (___ , ___)

5 Mark these letters on the grid.

a G at (**0, 3**)   b H at (**4, 2**)   c J at (**1, 4**)

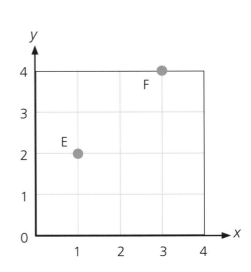

6 Tick any shapes that have reflective symmetry.

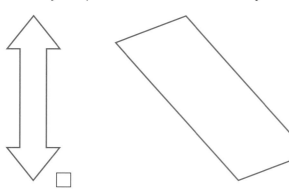

7 Write the co-ordinates of these letters.

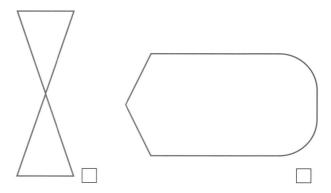

a P (____, ____)   **b** Q (____, ____)

c R (____, ____)   **d** S (____, ____)

8 Mark these letters on the grid.

a T at (**–4, 0**)   **b** U at (**4, –5**)

c W at (**–2, 2**)   **d** Z at (**–1, 5**)

9 Convert these measurements.

a 71m = _____ cm   **b** 725cm = _____ m   **c** 4230ml = _____ l

d 25l = _____ ml   **e** 3200g = _____ kg   **f** 6.75kg = _____ g

10 Colour the best estimate for each item.

a
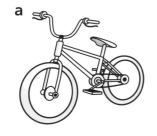

7kg
70kg
700kg

b
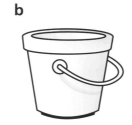

1l
10l
100l

c

30g
300g
3kg

11 Draw the same time on the matching clock.

a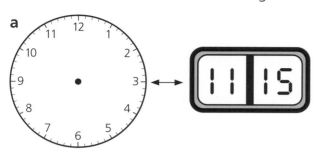

b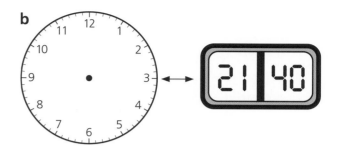

12 Find the area of these rectangles.

a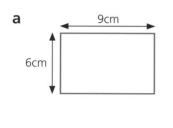

_____ cm²

b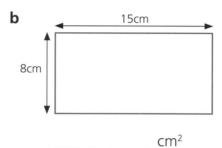

_____ cm²

c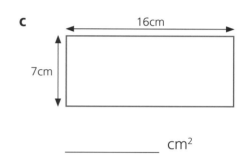

_____ cm²

13 Find the area of these shapes.

a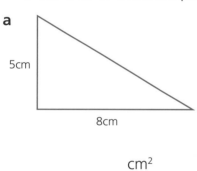

_____ cm²

b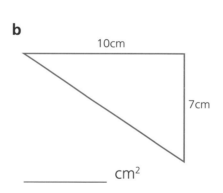

_____ cm²

c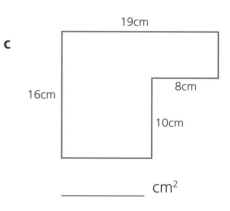

_____ cm²

14 Find the perimeter of these shapes.

a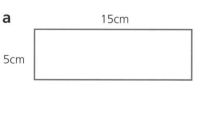

_____ cm

b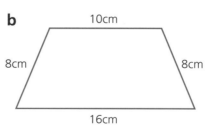

_____ cm

c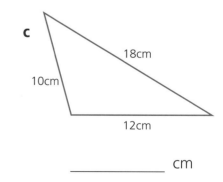

_____ cm

15 Write the numbers being pointed to on these scales.

a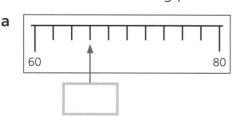

b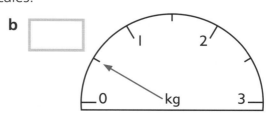

16 Calculate the missing angles.

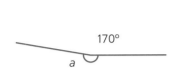

170°

a

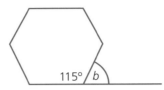

115° *b*

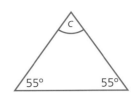

c

55°   55°

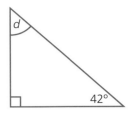

d

42°

a = _____

b = _____

c = _____

d = _____

17 Answer these questions.

a What is the name of the straight line from the edge
to the centre of a circle?

_____

b What is the name of the straight line from one side of
a circle to the other, passing through its centre?

_____

18 Convert between these units.

a **3** miles = _____ km

b **11** pints = _____ ml

c _____ ounces = **50**g

d _____ miles = **32**km

19 Find the volume of these cuboids using length, width and height.

a

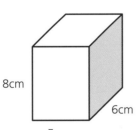

8cm

6cm

5cm

_____ cm³

b

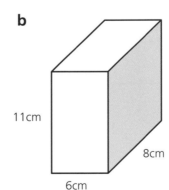

11cm

8cm

6cm

_____ cm³

20 Solve these problems.

a Kristen earns £**500** per month. How much does she earn in **3** years?    _____

b It is **9** weeks and **4** days until Nasir goes on holiday.
He decides to save £**1** each day until then to use as spending
money. How much spending money will he end up with?   _____

Answers to Activities

Page 5: 2-D shapes 2

1

Shape	Number of sides	Number of vertices	Straight or curved?
circle	1	0	curved
triangle	3	3	straight
rectangle	4	4	straight
square	4	4	straight
pentagon	5	5	straight
hexagon	6	6	straight
octagon	8	8	straight
decagon	10	10	straight

2 These three polygons should be coloured.

Page 6: Angles 1

1   **a** obtuse   **b** acute   **c** reflex

     d right   **e** obtuse   **f** acute

     g straight   **h** right   **i** reflex

Page 7: Triangles

1   **a** scalene

     b equilateral

     c isosceles

     d scalene

     e isosceles

     f isosceles

     g equilateral

     h scalene

2 **b** and **d** should be ticked

3 **h**

Page 8: Quadrilaterals

1   **a** P, S, T, U

     b P, S

     c S

     d T, S

     e Q, R

     f V, W

Page 9: Reflective symmetry

1

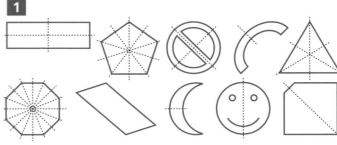

2

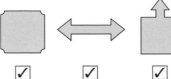

✓   ✓   ✓   ✓   ✓

Page 11: Co-ordinates 1

1   **a** (1, 4)   **b** (4, 2)

     c (0, 6)   **d** (2, 0)

2 J, K, L and M placed as shown:

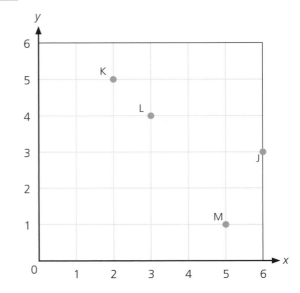

Page 12: Translations

1   **a**   (1, 1) (3, 1) (1, 5)

     b   (2, 0) (4, 0) (2, 4)

     c   (6, 3) (8, 3) (6, 7)

a 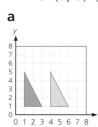   **b** 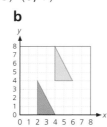   **c**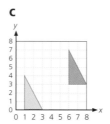

2   **a**   (3, 3) (4, 5) (7, 6)

     b   (1, 7) (2, 9) (5, 10)

     c   (0, 1) (1, 3) (4, 4)

Page 13: Angles 2

1   **a**   15°   **b**   138°

     c   50°   **d**   125°

     e   170°

Page 14: 3-D shapes 1

1   **a**   cone

     b   cylinder

     c   pentagonal prism

     d   cuboid or rectangular prism

     e   triangular-based pyramid
        (sometimes called a tetrahedron)

Page 15: 3-D shapes 2

1

Name of shape	Number of faces (F)	Number of vertices (V)	Number of edges (E)
sphere	1	0	0
cone	2	1	1
cylinder	3	0	2
cube	6	8	12
cuboid	6	8	12
triangular prism	5	6	9
square-based pyramid	5	5	8

2

Shape	F	V	E + 2
cube	6	8	14
cuboid	6	8	14
triangular prism	5	6	11
square-based pyramid	5	5	10

Page 17: Drawing and making shapes

1   Lines drawn correctly.

2   Angle drawn correctly.

3

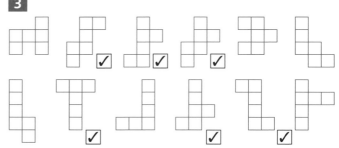

Page 18: Co-ordinates 2

1   **a**   (2, 1)   **b**   (5, –2)

     c   (–1, –3)   **d**   (–2, 0)

2   J, K, L and M placed as shown:

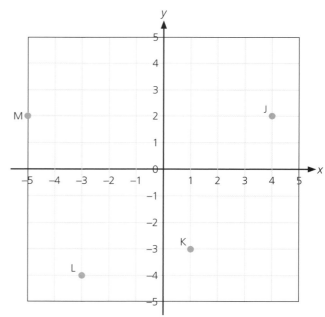

Page 19: Reflecting patterns and shapes 1

1 a   b   c

d   e 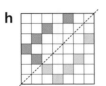 f

g h i

Page 20: Reflecting patterns and shapes 2

1 a (−3, 1) (−3, 4) (−1, 3)

b (3, −1) (3, −4) (1, −3)

2 and **3**

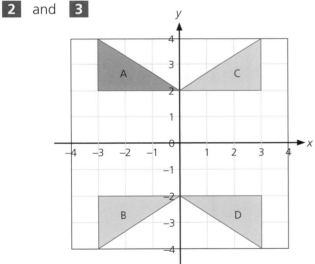

Page 21: Calculating angles

1 *a* = 240° *b* = 70° *c* = 40° *d* = 50°

2 a 67°, acute b 130°

c 35° d 26°

Page 22: Circles

1 a diameter

b 10cm

c 4cm

d 9cm

e 12cm^2

f chord

g sector

Page 24: Length

1 own results

2 a 15cm b 180cm c 17m

Page 25: Mass

1 own results

2 a 1kg b 30kg c 10kg

Page 26: Capacity

1 own results

2 a 250ml b 3ml c 5l

Page 27: Converting between units of measurement

1 a 6300cm b 4.5m c 3.17l
d 10 000ml e 4.5kg f 5250g
g 47.8m h 3.875l i 7.82kg

2 a 100 b 1000
c 1000 d 1000
e 10 f 1000

Page 28: Problems involving length, mass and capacity

1 a 5200g   b 1800ml

c 7kg   d 0.9l

e 5.2cm   f 23cm

g 13kg   h 8.5l

2 Answers may be given as an equivalent amount in a different unit.

a 600ml

b 240cm

c 30mm or 3cm

d 3800m

e 4000g or 4kg

f 65mm

g 500ml

Page 29: Reading scales

1 Answers may be given as an equivalent amount in a different unit.

a 4.6   b 2.5kg   c 700ml

d 13.6   e 1300ml

f 8.75   g 2.4kg

Page 30: Perimeter

1 a 36cm   b 50cm   c 60cm

2 a 24cm   b 32cm

c 34cm   d 64cm

Page 31: Time 1

1 a 6:53   b 11:44   c 8:02

2

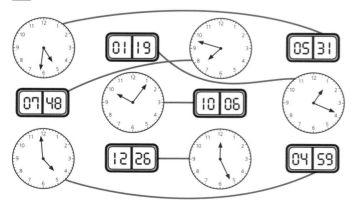

Page 32: Time 2

1

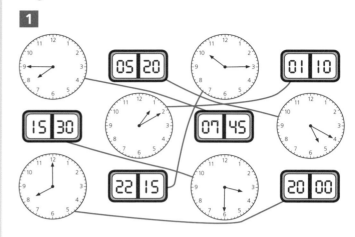

Page 34: Time 3

1 a days, weeks or months

b minutes

c years

d hours

e centuries

2 a half past seven in the evening or 7.30 p.m. or 19:30

b quarter to four in the afternoon or 3.45 p.m. or 15:45

c Screen 3

d *Jack Sprat*

Page 35: Area 1

1 a 12 squares

b 24 squares

c 20 squares

2 a 28cm²   b 40cm²   c 54cm²

Page 36: Imperial units

1 a 24 inches   b 12 feet

c 880 yards   d 16 pints

e 160 ounces   f 42 pounds

2 a 3.2km   b 45l

c 4 miles   d 70.4 pounds

Page 37: Area 2

1 **a** 20cm^2 **b** 30cm^2 **c** 108cm^2

2 **a** 203cm^2 **b** 208cm^2 **c** 450cm^2

Page 38: Volume

1 **a** 32cm^3 **b** 24cm^3

2 **a** 140cm^3 **b** 240cm^3
    c 132cm^3 **d** 216cm^3

Page 39: Time problems

1 **a** 120 seconds **b** 240 minutes
    c 10 days **d** 7 weeks
    e 20 weeks **f** 156 weeks
    g 20 years **h** 1095 days

2 **a** Saturday 4 p.m. or 16:00
    b £7200
    c £62

Page 40: Area and perimeter

1 **a** 12cm **b** 9cm **c** 5cm

2 **a** 48cm **b** 48cm **c** 38cm

3 **a** 116cm^2 **b** 71cm^2 **c** 64cm^2

Answers to Progress tests

PROGRESS TEST 1 – Page 10

1 **a** hexagon **b** decagon

2 **a** obtuse **b** acute **c** right

3 **a** isosceles **b** isosceles
 c equilateral **d** scalene

4 **c**

5 **a** trapezium **b** square
 c rhombus **d** kite

6 **b**

7
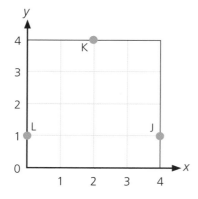

PROGRESS TEST 2 – Page 16

1 **a** (1, 3) **b** (2, 0) **c** (3, 4)

2

3 **a** (4, 4) (4, 6) (8, 6)
 b (2, 7) (2, 9) (6, 9)
 c (1, 2) (1, 4) (5, 4)

4 **a** 26° **b** 142°

5 **a** hexagonal prism **b** sphere
 c cone **d** cuboid or rectangular prism

6 **a** F = 6, V = 8, E = 12
 b F = 5, V = 5, E = 8
 c F = 8, V = 12, E = 18

PROGRESS TEST 3 – Page 23

1 **a**   **b**   **c**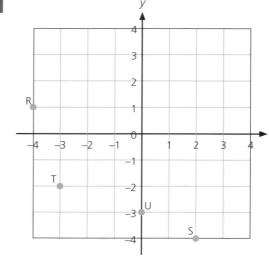

2 **a** (–2, 3) **b** (4, –3)

3
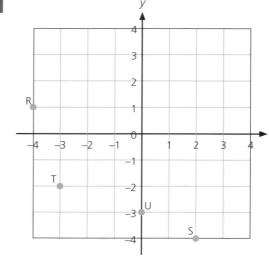

4 **a** = 250° **b** = 72° **c** = 50° **d** = 55°

5 **a** circumference
 b 3.5cm **c** 16cm

PROGRESS TEST 4 – Page 33

1 **a** 10g **b** 200l **c** 2kg

2 **a** 700cm **b** 25mm
 c 60cm **d** 800m

3 **a** 700ml
 b 3.4m or 340cm
 c 33mm

4 **a** 30cm **b** 35cm **c** 24cm

5
a

b

Answers to Final test

FINAL TEST – Pages 41–44

1 **a** obtuse   **b** reflex   **c** straight

2 **a** 25°   **b** 125°

3 **a** F = 6, V = 8, E = 12
   b F = 4, V = 4, E = 6
   c F = 7, V = 10, E = 15

4 **a** (1, 2)   **b** (3, 4)

5
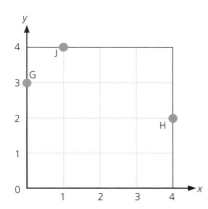

6
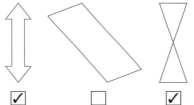
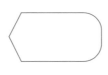

✓   ☐   ✓   ✓

7 **a** (2, −4)   **b** (−3, 2)
   c (4, 3)   **d** (−4, −4)

8
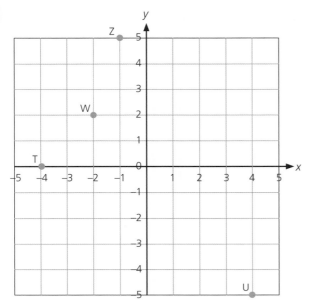

9 **a** 7100cm   **b** 7.25m   **c** 4.23l
   d 25000ml   **e** 3.2kg   **f** 6750g

10 **a** 7kg   **b** 10l   **c** 300g

11 **a**

   b

12 **a** 54cm²   **b** 120cm²   **c** 112cm²

13 **a** 20cm²   **b** 35cm²   **c** 224cm²

14 **a** 40cm   **b** 42cm   **c** 40cm

15 **a** 66   **b** 0.5kg or $\frac{1}{2}$kg or 500g

16 a = 190° b = 65° c = 70° d = 48°

17 **a** radius
   b diameter

18 **a** 4.8km   **b** 5500ml
   c 2 ounces   **d** 20 miles

19 **a** 240cm³   **b** 528cm³

20 **a** £18000
   b £67